WISDOM

GOD'S VISION FOR LIFE

Thomas Smith and Jeff Cavins

ASCENSION
West Chester, PA

Ascension Press
Post Office Box 1990
West Chester, PA 19380
1-800-376-0520
AscensionPress.com
ISBN 978-1-945179-15-0

Welcome to
The Great Adventure

"To fall in love with God is the greatest of all romances; to seek him, the greatest adventure." – St. Augustine

The Bible is at the heart of our Catholic Faith—and our relationship with God. It is the living Word of God, where our Father meets with us and lovingly speaks to us. Reading the Bible should bring us closer to Christ, but understanding it is not always easy. Many people tell us they have tried time and again to prayerfully read Scripture, but they get frustrated because they "just don't get it."

The Great Adventure is designed so that anyone can make sense of the Bible and experience the life-changing power of God's Word. At the core of *The Great Adventure* is the concept that there is a story running through the seventy-three books of the Bible that ties all of Scripture together and makes sense not just of the Bible, but of our lives as well.

That story is God's plan as it has unfolded throughout salvation history and continues to unfold today. Once we grasp this "big picture," the readings at Mass begin to make more sense, our Scripture reading and study come to life, and we see how our lives fit into God's loving plan.

Hundreds of thousands of participants have discovered the riches of Scripture by experiencing one or more *Great Adventure* Bible studies. It is our prayer that you will gain a newfound understanding of God's Word that will transform your life and bring you closer to Christ.

Jeff Cavins, Creator & President,
The Great Adventure

Sarah Christmyer, Co-developer & Author,
The Great Adventure

About The Great Adventure Catholic Bible Study Program

At the core of *The Great Adventure* is *The Bible Timeline* Learning System: a simple way to get the "big picture" of the Bible by focusing on the story that runs throughout Sacred Scripture. *Great Adventure* Bible studies explore the biblical narrative in light of Catholic teaching and the historical, cultural, and literary context of the Scriptures in order to discover what Scripture reveals about God's plan and our place within it. Studies of individual books of the Bible are supplemented by thematic and "life application" studies.

Every *Great Adventure* study is designed to foster:

- Familiarity with the Bible and ease of reading it
- Bible study habits consistent with the guidelines of the Catholic Church
- Personal engagement in the Word of God
- Faith-sharing based on the Word of God
- Growth in knowledge about Scripture and the Catholic Faith

About *Wisdom: God's Vision for Life*

In everything from friendships to finances, making decisions to attaining peace of mind, Scripture offers a vision for happiness and well-being. Drawing on the "wisdom literature" of the Bible—Proverbs, Wisdom, Sirach, Ecclesiastes, Job, and the Wisdom Psalms—*Wisdom: God's Vision for Life* provides sound guidance on attaining wisdom.

Materials

- **The Journal** – Contains home reading assignments, engaging study questions, pages for *lectio divina,* talk notes for the video presentations, and responses to the questions. *(You will need one Journal for every participant, study leader, and small-group facilitator.)*

- **Video Presentations** (eight 30-minute sessions) – Presented by Jeff Cavins and other experts, these video presentations will help participants learn how to gather, gain, and grow in wisdom and experience the joy it brings to their lives. *(You will need one DVD Set.)*

In addition, every participant, leader, and small-group facilitator should have a Catholic Bible. We recommend the Revised Standard Version–Catholic Edition (RSV-CE).

How the Study Works

Every session in this *Great Adventure* study includes four essential steps, which are designed to fit together and build upon each other. Following these steps in order will allow you to get the most out of each session.

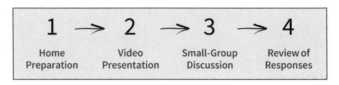

Step 1: Home Preparation

Note: There is no home preparation for Session One.

Each session in the journal begins with personal study on "Learning Wisdom" and "Living Wisdom." In these sections, you will read Scripture passages and answer a series of questions to help you understand and think more deeply about what you have read. Some questions will include additional reading from other parts of the Bible or from the *Catechism of the Catholic Church* (CCC) to help you consider the passage in light of the bigger picture of salvation history and Catholic teaching. We suggest that home preparation be done in several sittings over the course of a week. This will help you create a habit of daily Bible reading and prayerful meditation.

Each session of this study also includes a four-page *"Lectio with Wisdom"* section. Participants are invited to take four days during the week to meditate on the passages provided using the ancient prayer method of *lectio divina.* The steps of *lectio divina* are outlined on page 8.

Step 2: Video Presentation (30 minutes)

Each weekly session will begin with a video presentation featuring Jeff Cavins and other experts. These videos offer unique insights and profound connections that will help you gain a deeper understanding of the Bible's wisdom literature and its relationship to the Catholic Faith and your life.

Step 3: Small-Group Discussion (45-60 minutes)

One of the richest parts of a *Great Adventure* Bible study is the small-group discussion. During this discussion, you and the other members of your small group will have the opportunity to review and discuss your responses to the questions and share the insights you gained from your *lectio divina* time and the video presentation.

This small-group discussion will allow you to obtain a richer understanding of the readings and help you apply them to your life. Trained facilitators guide the small-group discussions and keep them on track. Be sure to follow the "Ten Commandments of a Small-Group Discussion" on page xvi.

Step 4: Review of Responses

The final step—reviewing the responses at the back of this journal—is done at home after the session and prior to beginning the reading for the next session. These responses will help you read the Scripture passages for the next session in the proper context.

For the richest study experience, complete these steps in order: (1) Read and answer the questions; (2) view the video presentation; (3) discuss your responses to the questions in your small group; and (4) review the responses.

> For more information about how to plan and promote a Bible study and how to facilitate a small-group discussion, visit **BibleStudyForCatholics.com/leaders,** or call our Study Consultants at 1-800-376-0520.

Session Outline and Reading Guide

Each session in this journal has the following sections. *(Note: The Introduction follows a different format.)*

1. **Session Questions** (used during **Step 1: Home Preparation** and **Step 3: Small-Group Discussion**)

    *   Introduction
    *   Learning Wisdom
    *   Living Wisdom
    *   *Lectio* with Wisdom

2. **Listening to Wisdom** (talk notes for use during **Step 2: Video Presentation**)

3. **Session Responses** (used during **Step 4: Review of Responses**)

The following chart offers an overview of the main home preparation readings assigned in each session of the study. Additional Bible readings and *Catechism* readings are provided in the questions section of each session and should be read as you answer the questions for that session.

Session	Title	Scripture Readings	CCC Reading
Session One	Introduction	Sirach 1:11-20	—
Session Two	Wisdom in Decision-Making	Sirach 9:14-15, 37:10-12; Proverbs 3:5-6, 3:21-26, 20:14-15; Tobit 4:19; Isaiah 11	CCC 1776–1789, 1831
Session Three	Wisdom in Finances	Proverbs 3:9, 4:10, 13:11, 14:31, 28:27, 29:7; Sirach 3:30-31, 8:12-13, 31:5-7, 40:19-27	CCC 2113, 2172, 2424, 2536
Session Four	Wisdom in Relationships	Proverbs 13:24, 14:26, 19:18, 22:6, 22:15; Sirach 6:5-7, 9:10	—
Session Five	Wisdom for Peace of Mind	Proverbs 19:11, 23:17, 24:1-2, 27:20, 29:11; Sirach 27:30; Wisdom 2:24; Philippians 4:4-9	CCC 2302–2306, 2538–2540
Session Six	Wisdom in Speech	Sirach 4:23-25, 5:10-14, 21:16-17, 28:12-16	CCC 2482–2487
Session Seven	Wisdom in Age	Psalm 78:3-7; 1 Timothy 5:9-10; Titus 2:1-5; Exodus 20:2-17; Sirach 3:1-16, 6:34, 7:27-28; Psalm 71	—
Session Eight	Wisdom in Christ	Matthew 5:21-26, 5:33-37, 6:1-18, 6:9-15, 7:24-27; Ephesians 4:26-27; James 1:19-20; 1 Corinthians 1:18-20	—

What to Do for Each Session

1. Welcome and Introduction (10 minutes)

2. Video Presentation (30 minutes)

3. Small-Group Discussion (45-60 minutes)

   Note to Study Leaders: During the first meeting, ensure that everyone has the study materials, explain how the study works, and divide participants into small groups of eight to twelve people. Each small group should be led by a trained facilitator. Have the small groups discuss the questions for Session One and read the Scripture passage provided.

4. Closing and Prayer (5 minutes)

Getting the Most Out of This Study

This study will help you understand the Bible in a new way. The "head knowledge" you gain will help you grow in "heart knowledge" as you follow up on what you have learned. The Bible will always remain a mystery, though, and that is part of the beauty of it: We can never exhaust the treasures of Scripture. Fortunately for us, the Bible is not a subject to master; it is a place to encounter the living Word of God.

Whenever you open your Bible to read, *start with prayer,* and place yourself in God's presence. You might take Samuel's prayer as your own: "Speak, Lord, for your servant is listening"

(1 Samuel 3:10). When you read, adopt an attitude of listening. Try not to treat Scripture as a text, but as a personal message from God. What is he saying? What does it mean? And what does it mean for your life? If you come to the Word focused on having an encounter with the Lord, he will speak to your heart, and you will be transformed.

Responses to the questions are provided in the back of this journal to help facilitators prepare for the small-group discussion and for participants to review after the meetings. Participants should not review the responses for each session until after the meeting. Although it might be tempting to look at these responses in advance, it is important to wait for the following reasons:

1. Bible study is not about simply watching a video presentation or reading a Bible commentary. It is just as important to immerse yourself in the Word of God itself and engage it with your heart and mind. The questions in *The Great Adventure* studies are designed to draw you into the Scriptures so that the Word of God will be planted and grow in your heart. Reading a response written by someone else may satisfy your mind for a moment, but it will not result in the kind of growth that will occur if you attempt to answer the question on your own first.

2. The success of a small group depends on a good discussion. A group of participants who have spent time pondering the Scripture passages on their own will have more varied insights to discuss.

When you follow the steps of this study as intended, you will explore the Word of God in different ways: in the reading, the video presentation, the small-group discussion, and, finally, in the responses. Follow these steps over time and you will be more than fed; you will learn to feed yourself.

Ten Commandments
of Small-Group Discussion[1]

1. Enjoy yourself!

2. Speak with respect and charity.

3. Do not ridicule or dismiss what others say. Keep comments positive.

4. Come prepared.

5. If you were not able to prepare, let others speak first.

6. Stick to the topic and questions at hand.

7. Start and end on time.

8. Allow silence. Give people a chance to think.

9. Listen to others without interrupting.

10. Keep personal matters within the group.

---

[1] Adapted from Thomas Smith's original "10 Commandments of a Small Group."

*" If any of you
lacks wisdom,
let him ask God,
who gives to all men
generously and without
reproaching, and
it will be given him."*

James 1:5

Session One

Introduction

Information Overload

Experts estimate that we now have more than 1.3 trillion gigabytes of online information at our fingertips. That's the equivalent of a stack of fully loaded iPads 339 miles high. When information is that ubiquitous, it can begin to consume our lives, giving us "paralysis by analysis." Much of this information is disposable and is forgotten within minutes. So, we may possess more information than ever before while never becoming truly wise.

Divine Data Collection

People in biblical times collected information, too, but it was data of a different kind. They received time-tested knowledge, which, when rightly applied, led to a life of wisdom and happiness.

Biblical wisdom is more than tweet-sized aphorisms or biblical "life-hacks" for practical living. For the authors of the Bible, wisdom was a matter of life and death. It was a carefully learned skill. In fact, the Hebrew word used for "wisdom" in the Old Testament, *chokmah,* was also used to describe the creative gifts of a temple artist (see Exodus 35:31), a skilled sailor (see Psalm 107:27), or a master goldsmith (see Jeremiah 10:9). In each case, these experts first had to apprentice under a master. They had to learn discipline and accept reproof and correction humbly.

If we want true wisdom, the journey is the same for us (see Proverbs 1:2-6). It requires a willingness to learn, an eagerness of spirit, and a humility of heart (see Proverbs 1:23, 15:33). Are you ready? Let's get started!

Sitting at the Feet of Wisdom

Few of us have the advantage of spending time at the feet of a true spiritual master, but Sacred Scripture gives us that opportunity. Ancient authors collected the greatest wisdom of their times, eventually committing it to written form so that we could hear and benefit from those sages today.

In this study, we will draw from many of the wisdom books of the Old Testament, including Proverbs, Wisdom of Solomon (commonly called the "book of Wisdom"), Sirach, Ecclesiastes, Job, and even the Wisdom Psalms.

Reading Wisdom Literature

The wisdom literature of the Bible is often in the form of proverbs: short, memorable statements, often with a contrasting parallel line. For example, "A wise man is cautious and turns away from evil, but a fool throws off restraint and is careless" (Proverbs 14:16). This literary design drives the point home and aids in memorization. Other times, the literature offers practical, godly advice: "The greater you are, the more you must humble yourself; so, you will find favor in the sight of the Lord. For great is the might of the Lord; he is glorified by the humble" (Sirach 3:18-20).

Wisdom literature is based on general principles of living. Individual wisdom sayings do not represent a guarantee or a promise. Proverbs 22:6 says, "Train up a child in the way he should go, and when he is old he will not depart from it." Overall, that is true. It should motivate parents to provide a thorough religious education for their children; however, there is no guarantee that your children will follow that instruction throughout their lives. Every human being has free will to choose his or her own destiny. So, we can see that this literature not only *teaches* wisdom but also *requires* some basic wisdom to navigate it successfully. Throughout this eight-part program, we will endeavor to help you do just that.

In this first session, take a moment to introduce yourself to your small group, review the "Ten Commandments of Small-Group Discussion" on page xvi, and discuss the following questions:

1. What, if any, experience do you have with Old Testament wisdom literature? Have you read or studied it before?

_____

_____

_____

_____

_____

_____

_____

2. Describe a wise person in your life who has helped you with important decisions or difficult situations.

_____

_____

_____

_____

_____

_____

3. What (or who) have been your sources of wisdom in life?

_____

_____

_____

4. Where do most people look for wisdom today?

_____

_____

_____

_____

5. What do you hope to gain from this *Wisdom* study?

_____

_____

_____

_____

_____

_____

_____

6. The Bible repeatedly reminds us that "to fear the LORD is the beginning of wisdom" (Sirach 1:14; see also Proverbs 1:7; Wisdom 12:11; Psalm 111:10). This attitude is not a frightened, servile submission to God, but rather a humble trust in his loving providence and protecting power. Read **Sirach 1:11-20** together as a group. What are the characteristics, blessings, and benefits of "the fear of the LORD"?

_____

_____

_____

_____

_____

_____

_____

_____

_____

_____

Wisdom in Your Week

The invitation to fear the Lord reminds us of who should be at the center of our lives—and in control. In the coming week, ask yourself regularly, "Who is in the driver's seat; who is on the throne?" If you can say God and God alone, that is the beginning of wisdom.

In addition to the Learning Wisdom and Living Wisdom sections included in each session in this journal, talk notes (Listening to Wisdom) are included to help you follow along with the video presentation. A Profiles in Wisdom feature in each session focuses on people from Church history who have exemplified wisdom in their own lives.

Lectio Divina

Four pages in each session are dedicated to the practice of *lectio divina,* which is a way of praying with the Bible. In *lectio divina,* a person chooses a short passage of Scripture and prays with it. The following steps of *lectio divina* are taken from *Praying Scripture for a Change: An Introduction to Lectio Divina.*[1]

1. **Read** *(lectio):* Slowly read a Scripture passage several times, paying close attention to the words.

2. **Reflect** *(meditate, meditatio):* Meditate on the Scripture passage, thinking about specific words or ideas that stand out to you.

3. **Relate** *(pray, oratio):* Converse with God about the Scripture passage and its meaning for you.

4. **Rest** *(contemplate, contemplatio):* Sit quietly in God's presence, enjoying just being with him.

---

[1] Tim Gray, *Praying Scripture for a Change: An Introduction to Lectio Divina* (West Chester, PA: Ascension Press, 2009), 36.

Wisdom from Father to Son

In ancient times, family authority and national leadership were passed on from father to son. This domestic dynamic was also the pattern for teaching wisdom (see Proverbs 1:8; Sirach 2:1). Much of our Old Testament wisdom literature was what a king would pass on to the heir of his throne. However, the use of masculine language should not lead us to believe that women were excluded from receiving or offering wisdom. Young people were taught to obey the instructions of their mothers (see Proverbs 6:20; Sirach 3:2) and to honor and respect the wisdom of both their parents (see Sirach 3:11, 7:27, 23:14). In fact, one of the most quoted sections of the Bible is the instruction given by the queen mother to her son, the king (see Proverbs 31). The wisdom of God is offered to anyone who will receive it, regardless of age or gender.

Listening to Wisdom
– Session One Talk Notes –

I. Introduction

  A. You and the world were created with wisdom (CCC 295); you need wisdom

  B. God's creatures are meant to share his being, wisdom, and goodness (CCC 295)

  C. Jesus is the Truth and the Wisdom (CCC 216)

  D. Wisdom pervades all things and helps us in all aspects of life (Wisdom 7:17-26)

II. Sources of Wisdom

  A. Wisdom defined

  1. The right application of knowledge, resulting in an integrated, fruitful, and holy life

2. The skill of living life from God's perspective

3. Prudence: synonym for wisdom (CCC 1806)

B. The foundation of wisdom

   1. "The fear of the Lord" (Proverbs 9:10)

   2. Humility

   3. Jesus is Wisdom (Colossians 2:3; Mark 6:2; Revelation 5:12, 7:12)

C. Relationship between knowledge, wisdom, and understanding

   1. Knowledge is "information gained through experience, reasoning, or acquaintance"

2. Wisdom is "the ability to discern or judge what is true, right, or lasting"

   a. Knowledge can exist without wisdom, but not the other way around

   b. A person can be knowledgeable without being wise

   c. Knowledge is the ability to use a gun; wisdom is knowing when to use it

3. When we walk in wisdom, understanding follows

D. The value of wisdom (Proverbs 2:3-4, 8:10-11, 23:23)

E. Worldly wisdom versus godly wisdom

F. Wisdom books

1. Proverbs – Solomon: Wisdom gave order to chaos and gives order to our lives

2. Sirach (book of Ecclesiasticus) – ethical teachings from approximately 200–175 BC

3. Ecclesiastes – ascribed to Solomon: a search for happiness

4. Wisdom – Wisdom of Solomon: Wisdom is personified

5. Job – typically included in the wisdom literature

6. James – the New Testament proverbs

III. Conclusion

A. Transform your mind (Romans 11:33–12:2)

B. The qualities of wisdom (James 3:13-17)

Session Two

Wisdom in Decision-Making

Introduction

Decisions. Decisions. Decisions. The average adult makes more than thirty thousand decisions a day. Many are made almost unconsciously, like our morning routine. Others are carefully deliberated, like a significant contract at work. And some are heart-wrenching, like an end-of-life decision for a loved one.

What are the principles that guide us in making those most important life decisions? In this session, we will explore the biblical principles for making decisions and how these spiritual guidelines can deepen our ongoing relationship of trust with the Lord and give us the courage to act.

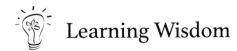 **Learning Wisdom**

1. Read **Sirach 9:14-15 and 37:10-12; Proverbs 3:6 and 20:14-15; and Tobit 4:19.**

   a. What principles of decision-making are discussed in these passages?

   _____

   _____

   _____

   _____

   _____

   b. Which passage struck you most, and why?

   _____

   _____

   _____

   _____

   _____

   _____

2. Sacred Scripture and the Catholic Church identify seven gifts of the Holy Spirit given to us at baptism and strengthened at confirmation. Read **Isaiah 11** and **CCC 1831.** Reflect on these gifts in the light of godly decision-making. How would the cultivation of these gifts help you when you are facing difficult choices?

_____

_____

_____

_____

_____

_____

_____

_____

_____

_____

_____

3. Read **Proverbs 3:5-6, 21-26.** Undue anxiety often keeps us from making decisions. What wisdom do these Scripture passages offer us?

_____

_____

_____

_____

_____

4. Having a well-formed conscience is indispensable in the Christian life. Review what the Church teaches about the conscience in **CCC 1776–1785,** and then use **CCC 1786–1789** to identify the factors necessary for making good judgments. What struck you most about these passages from the *Catechism?*

_____

_____

_____

_____

_____

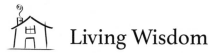 **Living Wisdom**

5. This week, apply some of the principles discussed in this session to a decision you need to make (it doesn't have to be a big one), and then answer the following questions.

    a. Which one of these principles is the most difficult for you to follow?

    _____

    _____

    _____

    _____

    _____

    b. What did you learn from using this process of decision-making? Be prepared to share your experience with your small group.

    _____

    _____

    _____

    _____

    _____

Lectio with Wisdom

Using the four-part model for *lectio divina* described on page 8, choose four days this week to meditate on the verses from Wisdom 9 provided on the following pages. Taken together, these verses are traditionally called the "Prayer of Solomon." Record any insights or memorable meditations you have.

Day One
Wisdom 9:1-6

Day Two
Wisdom 9:7-9

Day Three

Wisdom 9:10-12

_____

_____

_____

_____

_____

_____

_____

_____

_____

_____

_____

_____

_____

Day Four
Wisdom 9:13-18

Wisdom in the Word

Although the wisdom literature is a distinct genre in the Bible, it is present throughout salvation history. Chapter 10 in the book of Wisdom shows wisdom at work in the story of salvation from Adam to Moses and demonstrates how the wisdom of God was present, especially in the Exodus narrative (see Wisdom 11–12). Similarly, Sirach praised God's majesty and power as displayed in the works of creation (see Sirach 42:15–43:33) and sang a hymn to his ancestors. Beginning with Enoch, this wisdom song spans the biblical timeline up to Simon in the period of the Maccabees, highlighting the key prophets, priests, and kings of salvation history (see also Sirach 44–50). These verses provide valuable insights and details.

Profiles in Wisdom

Ten Tips on Decision-Making from St. Ignatius of Loyola

We all need to see concrete examples of wise living. St. Ignatius of Loyola (1491–1556), the fiery founder of the Jesuits, is a perfect guide for making smart decisions. His rich advice on decision-making, found in his *Spiritual Exercises,* is too vast to include here, but the following ten tips from this prayerful saint can help us.

1. The first principle of good decision-making is to ensure you are choosing between two goods: *Should I get married or become a priest or religious?* The question, *Should I cheat on my taxes?,* would be the wrong question.

2. Pray for the grace that your chief desire will be to love and serve God faithfully. Any individual choice must be seen through that relational paradigm and should set you on the course that helps you best serve God.

3. Be alert. There will always be struggle and internal conflict. Sometimes this will reach the level of spiritual warfare. Our false human ego, habitual sin, fears, and outside spiritual influences are often at play in making important decisions.

4. Set your choices before your mind clearly.

5. Pray for the grace to be objective about the choices in front of you. Do not come to the Lord with your mind already made up looking for him to confirm your choice.

6. Identify the "pros" and "cons" of each path. Looking ahead to the end of your life, which choice would serve the Lord best?

7. Seek the wise counsel of a mature Christian, spiritual director, or trusted mentor.

8. Having done all this, make an objectively reasoned judgment and ask the Lord to give you a confirmation. A sense of peace, joy, and "rightness" after making the decision should be present. If you still feel doubt, anxiety, or heaviness of heart, this may indicate that the choice was not a wise one and that you need to review the steps above with the help of a trusted friend or mentor.

9. If your decision is confirmed by a sense of peace, take a concrete "next action" toward that end and watch for further direction from the Lord.

10. Finally, don't forget that although there may be difficulties ahead, God desires your happiness and fulfillment.

Listening to Wisdom
– Session Two Talk Notes –

I. Introduction

   A. Do you live by godly principles or personal preferences? (Psalm 37:4; CCC 1768; Wisdom 7:27)

   B. The place of decision

      1. In the heart: in a covenant relationship with God (CCC 1768)

      2. In the Holy Spirit (John 16:13)

      3. In Scripture and Tradition (Psalm 119:105)

   C. Decisions are an act of the will

II. Practical Steps in Decision-Making

    A. Ask for help (James 1:5)

    B. Gather the important data

        1. Search for everything you can find (knowledge) on the topic (Proverbs 13:16)

        2. Study of God's Word, prayer, and counsel

    C. Talk to knowledgeable people (Proverbs 24:6, 11:14, 18:1)

    D. Consider the cost

        1. Ask yourself, "What will this decision cost me?"

2. Think about your time, money, resources, and gifts (Proverbs 19:12)

E. How is it going to affect your vocation?

F. How does your experience play into this decision? (Proverbs 26:11)

G. Consider your family background

H. Consider your reputation and witness (Proverbs 22:1, 25:26)

I. Don't wait for perfection (Ecclesiastes 11:4)

J. Act on your decision (Matthew 7:24-27)

III. Conscience

A. Everyone has an obligation to form his or her conscience (CCC 1798)

B. A well-formed conscience is formed by God's Word, principles not preferences

IV. Conclusion

A. All of life is a decision-making process

B. God will give you peace in making decisions (Philippians 4:7)

Session Three

Wisdom
in Finances

Introduction

Most Catholics would be surprised to learn that Jesus spoke more about finances than nearly any other topic. Around one-quarter of his parables in the Gospels address the wise use of resources. Jesus spoke of smart stewardship, long-term planning versus short-term gain, investing, hoarding, supporting the poor generously, the dangers of wealth, and even paying taxes. He was not concerned only about what his followers possessed, but rather what possessed them. As a faithful Jew, Jesus was familiar with the rich wisdom on finances from the Old Testament and drew from this to teach his disciples.

Though we have made many advancements in the exchange of goods and services since the time of the Bible, the wisdom of Scripture on the topic of money is perpetually practical. And we desperately need to recover this wisdom. Today, finances are the leading cause of stress in our relationships with spouses, children, and aging parents. One study showed that arguing about money in marriage is the top predictor of divorce. Eighty percent of Americans are in debt—an eleven percent increase in the last decade. Less than half of U.S. citizens could write a five-hundred-dollar check. We need help, and we need hope. Let us turn our hearts and minds to the timeless wisdom of Scripture on the topic of our finances. This will be a wise investment of our time.

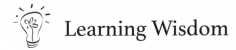 **Learning Wisdom**

1. Read **Proverbs 3:9, 13:11, 28:27, and 29:7 and Sirach 3:30-31, 8:12-13, and 31:5-7.**

   a. What wisdom do you discover on finances?

   _____

   _____

   _____

   _____

   _____

   _____

   b. Which passage struck you most, and why?

   _____

   _____

   _____

   _____

   _____

   _____

   _____

2. What attitudes toward money (both positive and negative) did you inherit from your parents, teachers, or mentors? How has that wisdom (or folly) influenced your approach to finances now?

_____

_____

_____

_____

_____

_____

3. Wealth can be a great blessing, but according to Scripture, there are possessions more valuable than money and much more readily available to us. Read **Sirach 40:19-27.**

   a. What are the blessings on this list?

_____

_____

_____

_____

b. Which blessing resonates with you most, and why?

_____

_____

_____

_____

_____

_____

_____

4. If it is not viewed in its proper perspective, money can become a kind of idol. **CCC 2113, 2172, 2424, and 2536** address the dangers of worshiping money. What can we learn from these passages?

_____

_____

_____

_____

_____

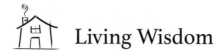 **Living Wisdom**

5. Charity and care for the poor are the marks of a wise person who understands the heart of the Lord. Read **Sirach 4:10** and **Proverbs 14:31.** What are a few ways your parish community is caring for those most in need of God's mercy? Participate in one of these ministries this week or make a concrete plan to give your time, talent, or treasure to one or more of them. Be prepared to share your experiences or intentions with your small group.

_____

_____

_____

_____

_____

_____

_____

_____

_____

_____

Lectio with Wisdom

Using the four-part model for *lectio divina* described on page 8, choose four days this week to meditate on the verses from Psalm 37 provided on the following pages. Although not traditionally included among the wisdom books of the Old Testament, some psalms have wisdom as their theme and can provide a rich harvest of insight. Record any insights or memorable meditations you have.

Day One
Psalm 37:1-7

_____

_____

_____

_____

_____

_____

_____

_____

_____

_____

_____

_____

_____

_____

Day Two
Psalm 37:8-20

_____

_____

_____

_____

_____

_____

_____

_____

_____

_____

_____

_____

_____

Day Three
Psalm 37:21-29

_____

_____

_____

_____

_____

_____

_____

_____

_____

_____

_____

_____

_____

Day Four
Psalm 37:30-40

_____

_____

_____

_____

_____

_____

_____

_____

_____

_____

_____

_____

_____

Offering the Lord Your First Fruits

"Honor the Lord with your substance and with the first fruits of all your produce; then your barns will be filled with plenty, and your vats will be bursting with wine" (Proverbs 3:9-10).

In the introduction to this study, we were reminded that the wisdom literature offers us principles, not promises that we can "take to the bank." Here is a case in point. In the Old Testament, obedience to God's covenant was tied to material blessings (see Deuteronomy 28:1-14). Rewards for righteousness and punishment for violations of the Law were immediate, concrete, and visible. It is comparable to training up a small child. In the New Covenant, we are discouraged from seeing material benefits as a reward for godly behavior (see 1 Timothy 6:3-6).

Even though we cannot guarantee blessings and we should not give expecting to be rewarded, we should give to the Lord the first and best of our resources, as the Israelites offered their first fruits. Additionally, we should be careful and thoughtful stewards of our remaining income, always using it in ways that honor God's name and plans. Though not expecting a reward, we can live with confident expectations that the Lord will provide for our needs as we "seek first his kingdom" (Matthew 6:33).

Profiles in Wisdom

St. Katharine Drexel (1858–1955)

The daughter of an international banker, Katharine was born into one of the wealthiest families in America. With a multi-million-dollar inheritance, educational opportunities at her family-founded university, and her choice of suitors, anything seemed possible for the young debutante. Philanthropy was a priority for her family, which donated millions annually to charitable causes. In addition, Katharine's stepmother regularly opened the family's home to feed and care for the poor. After a visit to the American West, Katharine marshaled her finances and influence to aid the plight of Native Americans living in desperate circumstances, even founding a school in Santa Fe, New Mexico.

Despite this, Katharine confided to her journal that she feared any kind of personal privation. It was a face-to-face encounter with Pope Leo XIII that would change the trajectory of her life forever. When she politely asked the pope to provide missionaries for the Native Americans, the pontiff pointedly asked, "Why don't you become a missionary?" Though shocked by his reply, she responded by renouncing her life of luxury and vast inheritance (estimated to be five hundred million dollars in today's economy) and using all her time, talent, and treasure to help those in most need of her mercy.

She founded the Sisters of the Blessed Sacrament and established fifty missions in sixteen states for Native Americans. She then turned her attention to the plight of African Americans, opening dozens of schools and mission centers in an additional thirteen states, including Xavier University, the first Catholic University in the United States for African Americans. Her generosity inspired the generosity of others, who opened their hearts and wallets for her causes. Mother Katharine Drexel died at age ninety-six. She was canonized in the year 2000 by St. John Paul II.

We may not be as well-off as St. Katharine was when she began her ministry, but it doesn't take millions to show mercy. We can give sacrificially of our time, talent, and treasure to worthy causes within our budgets, and our generosity can inspire others to act with kindness, mercy, and love.

Listening to Wisdom

– Session Three Talk Notes –

I. Introduction

A. We make decisions about money daily

B. Most of us have experienced worry over money
(Sirach 31:1)

II. Locate the Treasure in Your Life

A. Find what is valuable in your life (Matthew 6:21-24)

B. Pay attention to family: Where your treasure is, there
your heart is (Proverbs 27:23)

III. Change Our Relationship with Money

A. We are stewards, not owners

B. The earth and everything in it is the Lord's
(Psalm 24:1-2)

IV. What's Wrong with Money?

A. Money doesn't buy happiness (1 Timothy 6:10; Ecclesiastes 5:10)

B. Financial troubles can take a toll on us if we love money too much (Sirach 31:5-9)

V. Generosity

A. Almsgiving and care for the poor are the mark of a wise person

B. *Ayin-tovah* ("good eye"): people who see the needs of others and respond with mercy, generosity, and love; the person with a bad eye is stingy, selfish

VI. Debt

A. When we go into debt, we lose a portion of our freedom

B. We sell our freedom for what we think will make us happy

VII. Tips for Wise Money-Handling

A. Be faithful, day by day: Be consistent, invest wisely, and be diligent (Proverbs 13:11, 10:4)

B. Diversify (Ecclesiastes 11:2)

C. Spend below your income; create margin (Proverbs 13:7, 21:20)

D. Count the cost when planning (Luke 14:28)

E. Plan with Christ's will in mind (James 4:13-15)

VIII. Warnings About Money

A. Gambling – a sin against justice (CCC 2413)

B. Money seems to promise security, but real security is
in Christ (Luke 16:13)

IX. Honor the Lord by Giving

A. Honor the Lord with your wealth (Proverbs 3:9)

B. Avoid idolatry (CCC 2113)

C. Don't spend more on animals than people
(CCC 2418)

D. Remember the Sabbath (CCC 2172)

E. Sowing and reaping (Ecclesiastes 11:1; Galatians 6:7)

X. Conclusion

Being free from the love of money leads to contentment

Session Four

Wisdom
in Relationships

Introduction

We have many kinds of relationships in this world. The most important ones are within the family dynamic: parents, siblings, spouse, and children. Other relationships, like friendships, can mean the difference between a long, fruitful life and a path of destructiveness and even death.

As humans, we are hardwired to connect with others, to build relationships, to shape communities, and to work in solidarity. New technologies now offer us an unprecedented opportunity to form virtual relationships with people across the globe. Family members and friends thousands of miles apart can now easily communicate, and information and ideas can be shared effortlessly between students and scientists at opposite ends of the world. While amazing, there are dangers as we navigate this largely unexplored digital continent. In the words of Pope Benedict XVI, "If the desire for virtual connectedness becomes obsessive, it may in fact function to isolate individuals from real social interaction while also disrupting the patterns of rest, silence and reflection that are necessary for healthy human development."[1]

These new challenges for maintaining healthy, happy relationships invite us to reconnect with the time-tested, practical, and powerful wisdom of the Bible.

---

[1] 43rd World Communications Day, 2009.

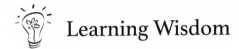 # Learning Wisdom

1. The first and most important relationship to cultivate is our relationship with God. **Proverbs 14:26** says, "In the fear of the LORD one has strong confidence, and his children will have a refuge" (also see Proverbs 20:7).

   a. Why is fear of the Lord—in our public and private lives—possibly the most important gift we can give our children and grandchildren?

   _____

   _____

   _____

   _____

   b. Share an experience where the lived faith of a parent, grandparent, or mentor helped your own budding faith to mature.

   _____

   _____

   _____

   _____

2. The discipline of children is a "hot-button" topic today. However, most people would agree that responsible parenting includes clearly defined and reasonable consequences for disobedient behavior (see Proverbs 29:15).

   a. Read **Proverbs 13:24, 19:18, 22:6, and 22:15** and record what you learn. According to the wisdom literature, why is disciplining children so important?

   _____

   _____

   _____

   _____

   b. Share how measured discipline received as a child positively shaped you or someone you know into adulthood?

   _____

   _____

   _____

   _____

3. Choosing good, wise friends is a common theme in the wisdom literature. The best friends are not only with us through good times and bad, but they help us see our spiritual blind spots. "Faithful are the wounds of a friend" (Proverbs 27:6).

a. Read **Sirach 6:5-17 and 9:10.** What do you learn from these passages about the importance of choosing good friends and mentors?

_____

_____

_____

_____

b. Describe the significance of solid friendships in your own faith life.

_____

_____

_____

_____

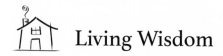 Living Wisdom

4. After reflecting on the topic of healthy, life-giving relationships this week, identify a relationship you want to improve. What is one thing you can do this week to nourish and strengthen that relationship?

_____

_____

_____

_____

_____

5. Take a few moments this week to reach out to a friend or family member (living or dead) and express your appreciation for his or her role in your life. Consider sharing your experience with your small group.

_____

_____

_____

_____

_____

Lectio with Wisdom

Proverbs 31:10-31 is a giant acrostic poem. Acrostic poems, in which each verse begins with a successive letter of the Hebrew alphabet, were designed for memorizing lengthy biblical texts. The poem in Proverbs 31 is a celebration of what St. John Paul II called "the feminine genius": "Far from representing an unattainable model, [the woman of Proverbs 31] is a concrete image born from the experience of women of great value."[2]

Using the four-part model for *lectio divina* described on page 8, choose four days this week to meditate on the verses from Proverbs 31 that are provided on the following pages. Record any insights or memorable meditations you have. You might use this session's *lectio divina* time to reflect on the importance of the wise women in your life.

---

[2] St. John Paul II, General Audience, April 10, 1996.

Day One
Proverbs 31:10-16

Day Two
Proverbs 31:17-22

_____

_____

_____

_____

_____

_____

_____

_____

_____

_____

_____

_____

_____

_____

Day Three
Proverbs 31:23-26

_____

_____

_____

_____

_____

_____

_____

_____

_____

_____

_____

_____

Day Four
Proverbs 31:27-31

_____

_____

_____

_____

_____

_____

_____

_____

_____

_____

_____

_____

_____

Wisdom in Love

In 1 Kings 4:32, we learn that King Solomon spoke three thousand proverbs and composed more than a thousand songs. Only one can be found in the canon of Scripture, the Song of Solomon (also known as the "Song of Songs" or "Canticle of Canticles"). The lyrical lines of this unusual text are a celebration of nuptial love between spouses, weaving a drama of courtship, separation, and embrace. Unlike Proverbs (which reflects a father in mid-life) and Ecclesiastes (which is thought to be a text composed by a man at the end of his life), the Song of Solomon reflects the heart of a young man. Hidden in the loving exchanges of the Song of Solomon is a deeper call for all of us. Among rabbinic commentaries, these verses were also seen as a love song between God, the divine Bridegroom, and his bride, Israel. This interpretation enriched Christian readers as they reflected on Christ's love for the Church. Consider reading the Song of Solomon as a fitting complement to the more practical insights you are gaining in this study.

Profiles in Wisdom

Saints Louis and Zélie Martin

Unfortunately, the names of Louis Martin (1823–1894) and Zélie Martin (1831–1877) are not widely known by Catholics, but their relative obscurity in no way diminishes their importance. They are, after all, the first married couple raised to sainthood together in the Catholic Church. They were the parents of a Doctor of the Church, St. Thérèse of Lisieux, the "Little Flower." Their four other daughters also became nuns. The saintly causes of Thérèse's remarkable sisters, Mother Agnes of Jesus, Sister Marie of the Sacred Heart, Sister Francoise-Therese, and Sister Genevieve of the Holy Face, are also being promoted for sainthood by the Sisters of the Visitation. This extraordinary fruit came from a family that expressed its love of God and the poor through the actions of its everyday lives together.

At their canonization, Pope Francis said, "The holy spouses Louis Martin and Marie-Azélie Guerin [Zélie] practiced Christian service in the family, creating day by day an environment of faith and love which nurtured the vocations of their daughters."[3]

Our own families may look very different than St. Thérèse's family, but the call to holiness is the same. We can be encouraged that although Louis and Zélie lived busy lives (both parents were business owners), they found "little ways" to cultivate faith, hope, and love throughout the day with each other and in those they encountered.

---

[3] Pope Francis, canonization homily for Louis and Zélie Martin, October 18, 2015.

Listening to Wisdom
– Session Four Talk Notes –

I. Introduction

    A. Relationship with God

    B. Relationship with one another

    C. Relationship with creation

II. Family

    A. Husband and wife

        1. Delight in your spouse (Proverbs 5:18-19)

        2. Your spouse is a gift from God (Proverbs 19:14)

3. Prefer one another (Ephesians 5:22-23)

4. Build your home on wisdom (Proverbs 24:3)

B. Parenting

1. *Chokmah* – wisdom; teach your children God's Word (Deuteronomy 6:6-9)

2. Children are not hard drives but gifts to be discovered (Proverbs 22:6)

3. Parents should reprove their children (Proverbs 3:12), but not provoke them to anger or discouragement (Ephesians 6:4)

III. Friendship

A. Close friendships make us happier and healthier

B. Wisdom helps us choose good friends

C. Friends love us at all times (Proverbs 17:9)

D. Choose wise friends (Proverbs 13:20, 27:17, 14:7, 23:20-21, 27:5-6)

E. Paradoxical statements

1. "Wounds from a friend": A friend must say painful but necessary words (Proverbs 27:5-6)

2. Hidden love: If we love our friends, we tell them the truth (Proverbs 29:5)

F. We become like our friends, so we must choose good ones (1 Corinthians 15:33)

G. Having a few deep friendships is healthy and wise (Proverbs 18:24)

H. Jesus is your friend and always loves you

I. Sirach 31:12-22 shows the practical wisdom of Scripture

IV. Conclusion

Make a few close friends and nurture the relationships

Session Five

Wisdom for
Peace of Mind

Introduction

The wisdom book of Ecclesiastes famously states that there is "a time to love, and a time to hate; a time for war, and a time for peace" (Ecclesiastes 3:8), and yet peaceful times seem to be a thing of the past. Endless wars, racial divisions, a fractious political culture, families in turmoil, and widespread anxiety all seem to be the "new normal" of modern life. Fortunately, real lasting peace *is* possible: It is found in the way of wisdom. "Her ways are ways of pleasantness, and all her paths are peace" (Proverbs 3:17).

In this session, we will learn how to walk the paths of peace, which lead us directly to the Prince of Peace: Jesus Christ. Famous Christian author Corrie ten Boom, who, along with her family, was imprisoned by the Nazis for helping Jews escape the Holocaust, said, "If you look at the world, you'll be distressed. If you look within, you'll be depressed. But if you look at Christ, you'll be at rest."

While there is not much we can do to directly address the absence of peace on a global scale, we can begin to solve the absence of peace in our own hearts: "Keep your heart with all vigilance; for from it flow the springs of life" (Proverbs 4:23). This session focuses on what often robs us of our peace on that heart level.

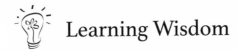

Learning Wisdom

1. Sirach reminds us that reverence of the Lord produces peace (see Sirach 1:18), and the psalmist confirms, "Great peace have those who love thy law; nothing can make them stumble" (Psalm 119:165). Share an example from a figure in Scripture or from your experience where rejecting God or disobeying him destroyed someone's peace.

_____

_____

_____

_____

2. Wisdom literature regularly reminds us that peace can be found, in part, through controlling our anger. Read **Proverbs 19:11 and 29:11** and **Sirach 27:30.**

   a. What do these verses reveal about the relationship between peace and anger?

   _____

   _____

   _____

   _____

b. The *Catechism* also connects these two realities (peace and anger). Read **CCC 2302–2306**. What do you discover about the relationship between personal peace and peace in our world?

_____

_____

_____

_____

_____

3. One of the other great thieves of our peace is the vice of envy. We can become consumed with what we do not have or envious of others and their possessions.

a. Read **Wisdom 2:24** and **Proverbs 23:17, 24:1-2, and 27:20** and record what you learn.

_____

_____

_____

_____

b. The Church shares its wisdom on the nature and dangers of envy in **CCC 2538–2540.** What do you discover from these paragraphs?

_____

_____

_____

_____

_____

4. St. Paul, a New Testament sage, was no stranger to difficulty and pain, yet he never lost his peace. Read **Philippians 4:4-9.** What wisdom does the apostle offer us for maintaining and sustaining our peace?

_____

_____

_____

_____

_____

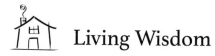 **Living Wisdom**

5. Jesus said, "Blessed are the peacemakers, for they shall be called sons of God" (Matthew 5:9). What are some concrete ways that we, as members of the Church, can promote peace in our parishes and communities?

_____

_____

_____

_____

6. Within the Mass, the priest prays that the sacrifice of Christ will "order our days in [God's] peace" and "advance the peace and salvation of all the world," and we are often challenged at the close of the Liturgy to "go in peace, glorifying the Lord by your life." How have the sacraments of the Church contributed to your peace and aided you in being a peacemaker?

_____

_____

_____

_____

Lectio with Wisdom

Using the four-part model for *lectio divina* described on page 8, choose four days this week to meditate on the passages from the book of Psalms provided on the following pages. Record any insights or memorable meditations you have.

Day One
Psalm 85:8-12

Day Two
Psalm 34:12-15

_____

_____

_____

_____

_____

_____

_____

_____

_____

_____

_____

_____

Day Three
Psalm 33:16-18

Day Four
Psalm 119:161-167

_____

_____

_____

_____

_____

_____

_____

_____

_____

_____

_____

_____

_____

Profiles in Wisdom

St. John XXIII – Pope of Peace (1881–1963)

More than fifty years ago, Pope John XVIII published *Pacem in Terris* (Peace on Earth). The groundbreaking document shared the Church's wisdom on everything from religious freedom and immigration to faithful citizenship and racial tensions. These peacemaking efforts by nations must be "founded on truth, built up on justice, nurtured and animated by charity, and brought into effect under the auspices of freedom."[1]

Although the pontiff praised every pursuit to establish peace in the world and to promote the common good, the Holy Father recognized that any lasting human peace depended upon the Lord:

> Finally, may Christ inflame the desires of all men to break through the barriers which divide them, to strengthen the bonds of mutual love, to learn to understand one another, and to pardon those who have done them wrong. Through his power and inspiration may all peoples welcome each other to their hearts as brothers, and may the peace they long for ever flower and ever reign among them.[2]

---

[1] *Pacem in Terris* 167.
[2] Ibid., 171.

Peace Offering

The author of Sirach mentions the peace offering twice (see Sirach 35:1 and 47:2; see also Leviticus 3:1-17 and 7:11-36). What was a peace offering, and what might be its significance for us today? If we hurt someone's feelings, we may offer them a heartfelt apology and a gift. In modern parlance, that is often described as a "peace offering." But in the Bible, a peace offering was given in a different situation. It was not meant to restore peace between parties, but to acknowledge an ongoing, established tranquility with God and others. It was a free-will expression of love and gratitude, not an attempt to repair a relational rupture.

This act was never obligatory, but rather the mark of a grateful soul; that is why it is described as "a pleasing odor to the Lord"

(Leviticus 3:5). That's "Bible talk" for the Lord's deep pleasure in this type of gift. In fact, St. Paul alludes to this offering in the New Testament: "And walk in love, as Christ loved us and gave himself up for us, a fragrant offering and sacrifice to God" (Ephesians 5:2). Jesus not only repaired our shattered shalom (peace) with God; his love expressed on the Cross is the ultimate peace offering with the Father and all of humanity. Every Mass is, therefore, a kind of peace offering. When we participate in the Liturgy, it is an expression of our gratitude for the ongoing peace established through Jesus for us. "May he give us gladness of heart, and grant that peace may be in our days in Israel, as in the days of old" (Sirach 50:23).

Listening to Wisdom
– Session Five Talk Notes –

I. Introduction

    A. Peace and total well-being: Shalom (John 14:27)

    B. Our inner compass is sometimes "off" (*Gaudium et Spes* 4, 8)

    C. We find peace when we walk in the wisdom of God (Proverbs 3:17, 4:23)

    D. Reconciliation is necessary for peace

II. How to Obtain Peace

    A. Obedience to God's Word (2 Samuel 15:2-26; Psalm 119:165; CCC 236)

B. Controlled anger (Proverbs 19:11, 29:11)

C. Resisting envy (Wisdom 2:24)

D. Forgiveness (Proverbs 16:7; Sirach 28:1; Proverbs 20:22)

E. Prayer (Philippians 4:6-7; Proverbs 2:3-5)

F. Taking thoughts captive (2 Corinthians 10:3-5)

III. Conclusion

You might not be able to control and change everything in the world around you, but you can control and change the world within you (Jeremiah 29:11)

Session Six

Wisdom in Speech

Introduction

It is often said that "talk is cheap," but words can be very costly. They have the power to bankrupt the strongest of relationships and have even started wars: "For every word in Hitler's *Mein Kampf,* 125 people lost their lives in World War II."[1] Words hold weight across our lifespan: We celebrate the first word spoken by a child, and we listen with rapt attention to the final words of a dying loved one. Talk, therefore, is not cheap. In fact, no one can put a price on the value of a word well-spoken (see Proverbs 25:11).

At their best, words are as valuable as gold and silver (see Proverbs 10:20, 25:11-12); compared to refreshing water (see Proverbs 18:4); a fountain of life (see Proverbs 10:11, 14:27); a tree of life (see Proverbs 15:4); nourishing food (see Proverbs 16:24); and a healing balm (see Proverbs 12:18). As we reflect on this week's topic, let us have the prayer of Sirach on our lips: "O that a guard were set over my mouth, and a seal of prudence upon my lips, that it may keep me from falling, so that my tongue may not destroy me!" (Sirach 22:27).

---

[1] Norman Cousins, quoted in Robert B. Downs, *Books that Changed the World* (Chicago: American Library Association, 1978), 285.

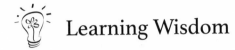 Learning Wisdom

1. Share an experience when you were hurt by someone's words and a time when you were blessed by someone's words.

_____

_____

_____

_____

_____

_____

2. The book of Sirach offers excellent advice on how to use the tongue wisely. Read **Sirach 4:23-25, 5:10-14, 21:16-17, and 28:12-16** and record the wisdom you find.

_____

_____

_____

_____

_____

_____

3. The book of Wisdom reminds us that a "lying mouth destroys the soul" (Wisdom 1:11). What additional insight does the Church offer us into the nature of dishonest speech? (See **CCC 2482–2487.**)

_____

_____

_____

_____

_____

4. The psalmist cries, "I have laid up [hidden] thy word in my heart, that I might not sin against thee" (Psalm 119:11). How can committing the Scriptures to memory and treasuring the Word in our hearts help us govern our speech?

_____

_____

_____

_____

_____

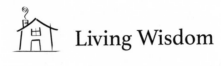 **Living Wisdom**

5. "Anxiety in a man's heart weighs him down, but a good word makes him glad" (Proverbs 12:25). Take a moment this week to write or call someone in your life whose good work is often overlooked and rarely thanked. Plan your words of encouragement and gratitude so you can communicate your appreciation clearly and confidently. Be prepared to share this or a similar experience with your small group.

_____

_____

_____

_____

_____

_____

_____

_____

_____

_____

6. Consider something you have said recently that was received by someone as hurtful or unkind. Take some time this week to reflect on that exchange in prayer, asking the Lord for insight into the situation. Then ask the Lord and the offended party for forgiveness. If you are comfortable, share this or a similar experience with your small group.

_____

_____

_____

_____

_____

_____

_____

_____

_____

_____

Lectio with Wisdom

Proverbs 12 turns our attention to the power of speech. Though short and simple, proverbs are powerhouses we can bring to prayer. Using the four-part model for *lectio divina* described on page 8, choose four days this week to meditate on the passages from the book of Proverbs provided on the following pages. Record any insights or memorable meditations you have.

Day One
Proverbs 12:6

Day Two
Proverbs 12:13

_____

_____

_____

_____

_____

_____

_____

_____

_____

_____

_____

_____

_____

_____

Day Three
Proverbs 12:19

Day Four
Proverbs 12:22

_____

_____

_____

_____

_____

_____

_____

_____

_____

_____

_____

_____

_____

_____

Who Wrote the Book of Proverbs?

While the book of Proverbs begins with the phrase, "The proverbs of Solomon, son of David, king of Israel" (Proverbs 1:1), the entire book was not composed by the king. Solomon is one of several authors spanning many generations. In fact, we only possess a small percentage of the three thousand proverbs the king composed (see 1 Kings 4:32). Proverbs 1–9:18 is a collection of general wisdom, while the proverbs in 10:1–22:16 are described as the "wise sayings of Solomon." "The sayings of the wise" comprise 22:17–24:22, followed by King Hezekiah's additions, which were selected by the royal scribes (see 25:1–29:27). The wisdom of Agur and the mother of King Lemuel are in Proverbs 30–31:1-9 and precede the completion of the collection—a stunning poem celebrating the ideal woman (see 31:10-31). Do you have a collection of wisdom gathered from wise people in your life? Make a concrete commitment to gather wisdom from the Scriptures and from the "sages" in your life.

Profiles in Wisdom

James the Just (d. AD 69)

Though the wisdom literature is a genre of the Old Testament, the New Testament is not without its own wise advice or sages. The epistle of James has long been regarded as a book of wisdom akin to Proverbs and Sirach. The author is most likely the close relative of Jesus, a special witness of the Resurrection, and a leader of the Jerusalem Church (see Mark 6:3; Galatians 1:19; 1 Corinthians 15:7; Acts 15:13-17).

His letter has many parallels with the Sermon on the Mount, a compact collection of the wisdom sayings of the Lord. As a leader, he recognized that words could establish or destroy the early Christian communities he shepherded. Like the authors of Sirach and Proverbs, James urged the followers of Jesus to be quick to listen and slow to speak (see 1:19), that true piety means controlling our speech (see 1:26), that the tongue can be poisonous and inflame others (see 3:6-8), and, most famously, that our deeds should match up with our words (see 2:14-24).

The most significant words we speak are those spoken in prayer, and James is fondly remembered as someone who spent many hours on his knees. Church historian Eusebius (c. 325) said:

> [James was] in the habit of entering alone into the temple, and was frequently found upon his knees begging forgiveness for the people, so that his knees became hard like those of a camel, in consequence of his constantly bending them in his worship of God, and asking forgiveness for the people.[2]

St. James, sage of the New Testament, pray for us!

---

[2]   *Church History of Eusebius,* II.23.6-7.

Listening to Wisdom
– Session Six Talk Notes –

I. Introduction

    A. Wisdom literature and the tongue

        1. Speech and the Tower of Babel (Genesis 11)

        2. Use the right words in the right circumstances (Proverbs 25:11)

    B. The problem with the tongue (James 3:2-10)

II. The Seriousness of the Tongue

    A. We speak what is in our hearts (Mathew 12:34)

    B. Our words have power (Proverbs 18:21)

C. Every person is accountable for his or her words
(Matthew 12:33-37; Proverbs 21:23)

III. Tearing Down

A. Four fundamental human rights: life, fidelity
in marriage, property, and reputation

B. Don't tear down your neighbors (Proverbs 11:9)

C. Six things the Lord hates (Proverbs 6:16-19)

D. Calumny and detraction (CCC 2477, 2479, 2477)

E. Warning to gossips (Proverbs 26:17-28)

F. Repeating a matter separates friends (Proverbs 17:9)

IV. Building Up

A. We can lift others up with our speech (Ephesians 4:29; Proverbs 12:18; Psalms 37:30)

B. We feel the desire to speak quickly, but we should stop ourselves before we attack (Colossians 4:6)

C. Use kind words (Proverbs 12:25; Psalm 39:1; Job 27:4)

D. Tone of voice is important (Proverbs 15:1)

E. Speak up for those who cannot speak for themselves (Proverbs 31:8)

V. Have a Plan You Can Practice

A. Ponder how you are going to answer
(Proverbs 15:28)

B. Practice being slow to speak (James 1:19-20;
Psalm 141:3)

C. Don't say a lot; say enough (Proverbs 10:19)

D. Have a cool spirit (Proverbs 17:27-28)

E. Don't speak prematurely (Proverbs 18:17)

VI. Conclusion

Your speech can build up, correct, comfort, and
encourage; give God control of your mouth (James 1:26;
1 Peter 3:10)

Session Seven

Wisdom in Age

Introduction

In 1917, the average life expectancy was forty-nine years. One hundred years later, we have added thirty years to the typical human timeline. By 2030, more than two billion people will be over the age of sixty (the combined populations of present-day India, continental Europe, and North America). Some sociologists view that trend with alarm, but the wise person recognizes that this means the world will hold the greatest reservoir of life experience and wisdom than at any other time in history. What a gift to the world if welcomed, celebrated, and accessed. "Wisdom is with the aged, and understanding in length of days" (Job 12:12).

Older people are often the guardians of our history, shared memories, ideals, and aspirations: "They still bring forth fruit in old age, they are ever full of sap and green" (Psalm 92:14). No matter what our age, we can all learn to "number our days that we may get a heart of wisdom" (Psalm 90:12) and grow in our appreciation of our elders, living intentionally with our own end in mind.

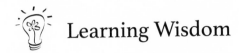 Learning Wisdom

1. According to divine revelation, what are the responsibilities of those who are mature in faith? Read **Psalm 78:3-7; 1 Timothy 5:9-10; and Titus 2:1-5.**

_____

_____

_____

_____

_____

2. Take a few moments to read through the list of the Ten Commandments in **Exodus 20:2-17.**

   a. Which of the ten commandments is the first to offer us a promise for keeping it?

_____

_____

_____

_____

_____

b. What is the promise, and why is that significant for us?

_____

_____

_____

3. A growing segment of our society is made up of children now caring for their older parents. What wisdom does **Sirach 3:1-16 and 7:27-28** offer them for embracing this opportunity?

_____

_____

_____

4. **Psalm 71** was written by a worshiper of advanced age. Spend some time reflecting on this song of praise. What wisdom can you glean from this ancient author?

_____

_____

_____

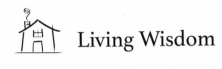 **Living Wisdom**

5. The book of Sirach advises us not to disregard what older people say because they, too, have learned from their parents (see Sirach 8:9). **Sirach 6:34** advises us to spend time with older people because they are wise. What are some practical ways you can engage mature Catholics in your parish?

_____

_____

_____

_____

_____

_____

_____

_____

_____

_____

_____

6. No matter what your age, you can share your wisdom
    with others:

    > God, you have taught me from my youth; to this day
    > I proclaim your wondrous deeds. Now that I am old
    > and gray, do not forsake me, God, that I may program
    > your might to all generations yet to come" (Psalm 71:
    > 17-18, NAB).

    Take some time this week to write a summary of the
    spiritual wisdom you have acquired so far in your life.
    It does not have to be lengthy. A written record of your
    spiritual wisdom will be treasured as one of the most
    important gifts you leave for those you love. Be prepared
    to share some of what you wrote with your small group.

    _____

    _____

    _____

    _____

    _____

    _____

Lectio with Wisdom

Using the four-part model for *lectio divina* described on page 8, choose four days this week to meditate on the Scripture passages provided on the following pages. Use the space provided to record any insights or memorable meditations you have.

Day One
Psalm 148:12-13

Day Two
Psalm 92:14

_____

_____

_____

_____

_____

_____

_____

_____

_____

_____

_____

_____

Day Three
Jeremiah 31:13

_____

_____

_____

_____

_____

_____

_____

_____

_____

_____

_____

_____

_____

Day Four
Joel 2:28

_____

_____

_____

_____

_____

_____

_____

_____

_____

_____

_____

_____

_____

Rediscovering Sirach

Though not widely known or read today, the "Wisdom of Ben Sir" (Sirach) was once universally known as *Liber Ecclesiasticus,* or the "Book of the Church" because of its extensive use in forming catechumens. Originally composed in Hebrew early in the second century before Christ, the book would later be translated into Greek by the author's grandson, who also included a forward regarding the book's authorship and origin. Over the last 120 years, Hebrew manuscripts were discovered in several places, including the famous fortress of Masada, supporting its claims and antiquity.

Sirach pictures the Wisdom of God (Torah) as a spiritual river, comparing it to life-giving waters (see Sirach 25:23-25). He views himself as a humble tributary of that wellspring of God's Word: "I went forth like a canal from a river and like a water channel into a garden. I said, 'I will water my orchard and drench my garden plot'; and lo, my canal became a river, and my river became a sea" (Sirach 24:30-31). His mission was to make God's instructions shine forth for all to see, gifting them to future generations, to all those "who seek instruction" (Sirach 24:34).

Profiles in Wisdom

St. Jeanne Jugan (1792–1879)

"Making the elderly happy—that is what counts!" This sentence reveals the heart of St. Jeanne Jugan, founder of the Little Sisters of the Poor. If you have ever visited a home staffed by this joyful congregation, you will see its motto in action. There are years-long waiting lists to get into one of their homes because of their extraordinary care and appreciation of the elderly, especially the poor. Jeanne grew up in France during a time of revolution, violence, and destitution. Because of the anti-religious government, she learned her Catholic Faith in secret meetings with other women. Raised by her widowed mother, she worked odd jobs to help support her family.

During a cold winter night, Jeanne met an elderly blind woman desperately trying to survive alone. Jeanne carried her home, laid her in her bed (while she slept in the attic), and cared for her until her death. This act of love was like the first pebble thrown in a pond, sending ripples of love that would spread to more than thirty countries around the world. In a time when many religious communities are dissolving, the Little Sisters of the Poor are flourishing 175 years after its founding. The sisters take a fourth vow of hospitality, viewing their patients as special guests whose wisdom is appreciated and whose final years are rewarded with love, dignity, and grace. At Jeanne Jugan's beatification, St. John Paul II said, "God could glorify no more humble a servant than she."

Listening to Wisdom
– Session Seven Talk Notes –

I. Introduction

A. Fear of growing old in the Western world (fear of gray hair)

B. Older people are often seen as a liability rather than an asset

C. Gray hair is like a crown; wear it proudly as a disciple of the King (Proverbs 16:13)

D. The old are acquainted with life's many seasons and can help the young

E. Clergy and religious deserve special honor (1 Timothy 5:17)

F. Older people are wise and wide in experience (Sirach 25:5-6)

II. Story and Wisdom

A. Wisdom is born of experience, not note taking

B. It is uncovered, discovered, and passed on by telling the stories of life

C. We tell stories to make a point, get a concept across, share a lesson learned, and teach

D. Older people are filled with stories children want to hear (Deuteronomy 11:19-21)

III. Practical Exercises

A. Write a letter to your children or grandchildren about what you have learned

B. Create a list of ten things you have learned to share with your children or grandchildren

IV. The Old Possess Wisdom and Sound Advice

A. Wisdom belongs to the aged and understanding to the old (Job 12:12)

B. Rehoboam received wise counsel from the elderly, not the young (1 Kings 12:6)

V. Wisdom Sticks when Health Fails

A. Habitual wisdom, especially in decision-making, endures

B. Despite aging, wisdom increases the feeling of well-being

VI. Show Respect to the Elderly

A. "Honor the face of an old man, and you shall fear your God" (Leviticus 19:32)

B. "Hearken to your father who begot you, and do not despise your mother when she is old" (Proverbs 23:22)

VII. Ways to Respect Your Elders

A. Give elderly people your time and assistance; visit them in nursing homes

B. Use good manners when speaking to them

C. Listen to stories about their lives; ask questions

D. Be patient with them and be a friend

VIII. The Value of Grandparents

A. They have time, money, and accumulated wisdom (Psalm 71:18)

B. Automatic respect for grandparents; grandchildren see them as a treasure

IX. Conclusion

Encouragement to the elderly: These are better days and you are not forgotten (Ecclesiastes 7:10; Isaiah 46:4; Psalm 71:18-19)

Wisdom in Christ

Introduction

In the introduction to this study, we learned that wisdom was pictured as a righteous person who calls us to the paths of holiness and good judgment (see Proverbs 8:1-7). This language helps us to see that we can have a relationship with wisdom by following its instruction as we would a wise teacher.

In the New Testament, the personified metaphor becomes an actual man. Jesus is Wisdom Incarnate. St. Paul says that in Christ are hidden "all the treasures of wisdom and knowledge" (Colossians 2:3). Jesus revealed God's wisdom not only in word but also in deed. His teachings displayed an authority and wisdom that astonished his audiences (see Mark 1:21-22, 6:2; Matthew 13:54; John 7:45-46), and his saving work on the Cross revealed the wisdom of God that the world perceived as folly (see 1 Corinthians 1:18-30).

This final session will help you reflect more deeply on Christ as our Wisdom and how he guides us in both word and deed to the pathways of life and happiness.

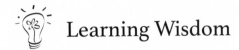 # Learning Wisdom

The Sermon on the Mount is widely regarded as the most compact and clear example of wisdom literature in the New Testament. It shares the characteristics of parallelisms, poetry, and vivid images that we have seen in the Old Testament texts, while demonstrating its superiority as God's definitive wisdom in Christ. While we will only explore a few themes from this stunning speech, you are invited to read the entire message in Matthew 5–7.

1. Read **Matthew 5:21-26.**

   a. What advice does Jesus offer regarding the passion of anger?

   _____

   _____

   _____

   b. Is there ever a time when anger is justified? Read **Ephesians 4:26-27** and **James 1:19-20.**

   _____

   _____

   _____

   _____

2. We learned in an earlier session that the power of life and death are in the tongue. Read **Matthew 5:33-37,** where Jesus specifically addresses honorable speech and oath-taking. According to Jesus, what are the characteristics of honest speech?

_____

_____

_____

3. In Matthew 6, Jesus shares his wisdom on piety and generosity.

   a. Read **Matthew 6:1.** What is Jesus' general principle for practicing faith?

_____

_____

_____

   b. Read **Matthew 6:2-18.** What are the three practices Jesus proposes for his followers?

_____

_____

    c. Though we often only associate these three practices with the season of Lent, in what way are they for all seasons, and what vices do they address?

_____

_____

4. What wisdom can you glean for prayer and the Christian life from the Our Father prayer in **Matthew 6:9-15?**

_____

_____

5. In St. Paul's first letter to the Corinthians, he compares the wisdom of God in Christ with the wisdom of the world. Read **1 Corinthians 1:18-30.**

    a. How are these perspectives different?

_____

_____

    b. Who will be the recipient of God's wisdom in Christ, and why is that significant?

_____

_____

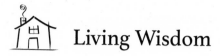 **Living Wisdom**

6. Jesus proclaimed that the person who listens to and obeys his Word is like a wise man who builds his house on a rock. Read **Matthew 7:24-27.**

 a. What parts of the Sermon on the Mount did you find most challenging, and why?

 _____

 _____

 _____

 _____

 _____

 b. Identify one concrete change you can make in your daily walk with the Lord based on the wisdom of the Sermon on the Mount. Be prepared to share it with your small group.

 _____

 _____

 _____

 _____

Lectio with Wisdom

Using the four-part model for *lectio divina* described on page 8, choose four days this week to meditate on the passages from Matthew 6 and 7 provided on the following pages. Record any insights or memorable meditations you have.

Day One
Matthew 6:25-34

Day Two
Matthew 7:1-5

Day Three
Matthew 7:7-11

_____

_____

_____

_____

_____

_____

_____

_____

_____

_____

_____

_____

_____

Day Four
Matthew 7:21-23

Profiles in Wisdom

St. Thomas Aquinas (1225–1274)

Thomas Aquinas, the medieval Dominican scholar and saint, is arguably the most famous intellectual in Church history. He was an ardent philosopher (lover of wisdom) and prodigious theologian, whom St. John Paul II called "an authentic model for all who seek the truth. In his thinking, the demands of reason and the power of faith found the most elevated synthesis ever attained by human thought."[1] In addition to the hundreds of pages of scholarship St. Thomas Aquinas gave the Church, the friar wrote many extraordinary prayers. Among them is a humble daily prayer for wisdom that students, seminarians, and scholars still intone today:

> Creator of all things, true source of light and wisdom, origin of all being, graciously let a ray of your light penetrate the darkness of my understanding. Take from me the double darkness in which I have been born, an obscurity of sin and ignorance. Give me a keen understanding, a retentive memory, and the ability to grasp things correctly and fundamentally. Grant me the talent of being exact in my explanations and the ability to express myself with thoroughness and charm. Point out the beginning, direct the progress, and help in the completion. I ask this through Jesus Christ our Lord. Amen.

St. Thomas Aquinas, lover of wisdom, pray for us!

---

[1] *Faith and Reason, 78.*

 # O Wisdom

O Come, O Wisdom from on high, who orders all things mightily, to us the path of knowledge show, and teach us in her ways to go.

During Advent, the Church sings the "O Antiphons" in preparation for the Nativity mystery. Among them is an address to Jesus as our Wisdom. According to Isaiah, the Spirit will give the promised Messiah seven gifts: wisdom, understanding, counsel, might, knowledge, piety, and fear of the Lord (see Isaiah 11:2-3). Because of God's great generosity, these seven gifts are not only for Jesus, but also for us. While their fullest expression belongs only to Jesus, he shares his wisdom with every baptized believer (see CCC 1830–1831). These gifts help us to be docile to the promptings of the Holy Spirit in our lives and give us the strength and courage to follow in Jesus' footsteps.

This session reminds us that Wisdom has a name: Jesus (see 1 Corinthians 1:30), and the chief way he shows God's wisdom is from the Cross (see 1 Corinthians 1:18-31). What does the Lord's offering on Calvary have to do with Christmastime and the Nativity? For Franciscans, the crib and the Cross are inseparable and often shown together in art. They both point to a divine wisdom that appears to be nothing but foolishness to the world. God comes both to the crib and Cross as a perfect gift of self: a full, free, fruitful, and faithful offering. In Bethlehem, his divinity is revealed in humility; on Calvary, life is found in death.

Listening to Wisdom

– Session Eight Talk Notes –

I. Introduction

A. Solomon possessed great wisdom, but Jesus' wisdom (in his teachings and parables) is greater than Solomon's (1 Kings 4:30; Luke 11:31; 1 Corinthians 1:30)

B. *Chokmah:* wisdom or counsel; practical advice for living

C. Jesus taught the disciples through Hebrew tradition; they did not view wisdom as mere information, but as the skill of applying knowledge to a specific area

II. Wisdom Is a Person: Jesus Christ

A. Wisdom is Christ (Colossians 2:3; 1 Corinthians 1:24, 1:30, 1:22-24)

B. James 3:13-18 describes wisdom/Christ as pure, peaceable, gentle, reasonable, full of mercy and good fruits, without uncertainty, and without insincerity

III. Take Jesus' Yoke

A. Taking his yoke is taking on his worldview (Matthew 11:28-29)

B. Christ promises rest and joy to disciples who walk in his wisdom (Sirach 6:23-31, 51:26-27)

IV. Becoming a Disciple

A. A disciple loves the Church because it teaches the splendor of Jesus' wisdom (Matthew 16; Ephesians 1:9-10)

B. Christ calls us to give up everything to follow him in his pattern of living: total self-gift (Mark 10:17-30)

C. A disciple prefers wisdom to wealth, health, and beauty (Wisdom 7:7-11; Psalm 90:12)

V. Get Wisdom (Proverbs 4:7)

A. Read the Bible: one chapter of Proverbs each day (thirty-one chapters)

B. *Do* God's Word (CCC 348)

C. Read the *Catechism*

D. Read encyclicals and Church documents

E. Listen to the elderly and to wise people; read about the saints

F. Pray: Spend time with Jesus (Proverbs 2:6)

G. Recognize your dependence on God: This is a source of wisdom (CCC 301)

H. Keep a journal of practical wisdom: Use it and pass it on

VI. Conclusion

A. "For whoever despises wisdom and instruction is miserable. Their hope is vain, their labors are unprofitable, and their works are useless" (Wisdom 3:11)

B. "The beginning of wisdom is the most sincere desire for instruction, and concern for instruction is love of her" (Wisdom 6:17)

C. "For she is a breath of the power of God" (Wisdom 7:25)

Responses
to the Study Questions

How to Use These Responses

After completing the home preparation, viewing the video presentation, and discussing the questions, the final step is to review the responses to the questions. These responses summarize the main points from the session and help you continue your Bible study in the next session.

Although it can be tempting to read these responses ahead of time, please wait until after you have completed the questions for each session and engaged in the small-group discussion. It is not necessary to have the "right" answers before going to the small-group discussion. In fact, one purpose of the discussion is for participants to learn by sharing their insights and questions with each other and, through that discussion, coming to a better understanding of the Scripture passages. This makes for a better Bible study experience for everyone.

For best results, follow these steps in order:

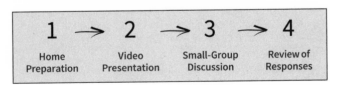

Introduction

1. *What, if any, experience do you have with Old Testament wisdom literature? Have you read or studied it before?*

Exposure to wisdom literature will range from lifelong students to those who are studying it for the first time. Small groups can be a wonderful way to grow by learning from one another's experiences—both from those deeply familiar with the content and from those who bring fresh eyes to the material.

2. *Describe a wise person in your life who has helped you with important decisions or difficult situations.*

Hopefully, we have all been blessed to have at least one wise person near to us. Sometimes it is a parent or family member, a trusted friend, clergy or religious, or even a stranger the Lord sends to speak into our lives.

3. *What (or who) have been your sources of wisdom in life?*

Sources of wisdom may include Sacred Scripture and Sacred Tradition, meaningful textbooks, spiritual literature, teachers, mentors, friends, and our lived experiences.

4. *Where do most people look for wisdom today?*

   Believers look primarily to divine revelation and to people who are well-versed in biblical wisdom, but in the broader population, many people turn to self-help books, social media, and the lives of celebrities, successful business people, or television gurus.

5. *What do you hope to gain from this* Wisdom *study?*

   Each person will approach this material with his or her own unique goals. We can appreciate one another's spiritual journey and perspective as we enter the Word of God together.

6. *The Bible repeatedly reminds us that "to fear the Lord is the beginning of wisdom" (Sirach 1:14; see also Proverbs 1:7; Wisdom 12:11; Psalm 111:10). This attitude is not a frightened, servile submission to God, but rather a humble trust in his loving providence and protecting power. Read* **Sirach 1:11-20** *together as a group. What are the characteristics, blessings, and benefits of "the fear of the Lord"?*

The fear of the Lord brings "glory" (honor, magnificence, and beauty[1]) and "exultation," which is "gladness and joy and long life" (Sirach 1:12). It also brings the blessing of God at the time of death. Wisdom is offered to us as a companion from the beginning of human life: "She is created with the faithful in the womb" (Sirach 1:14). Wisdom is a spiritual foundation that can be trusted for generations. The wisdom of God brings fruitfulness and bounty to the lives of those who fear the Lord. "The fear of the Lord is the crown of wisdom, making peace and perfect health to flourish" (Sirach 1:15). In Sirach 1:16, we read that wisdom is personified as a wise woman, and that those who hold wisdom close receive knowledge, discernment, and comprehension. Finally, the author compares the fear of the Lord to the roots of a great tree: "To fear the Lord is the root of wisdom, and her branches are long life" (Sirach 1:20).

---

[1] These three words make up the definition for *hadar*, the Hebrew word for "glory," as defined in James Strong, *Strong's Hebrew Dictionary of the Bible* (New York: Abingdon Press, 1890), no. 1926.

Session Two

Wisdom in
Decision-Making

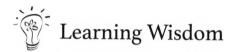 Learning Wisdom

1. *Read* **Sirach 9:14-15 and 37:10-12; Proverbs 3:6 and** **20:14-15; and Tobit 4:19.**

   a. *What principles of decision-making are discussed in* *these passages?*

   Sirach recommends that we consult with wise people and that we should talk about the Word of God, "the law of the Most High" (Sirach 9:15). In 37:10-12, he tells us not to seek wisdom from those who are suspicious of us or jealous of our lives or plans, because these things could cloud their judgment. Sirach then gives practical advice for choosing wise counselors carefully. For example, if you want to speak about mercy, turn to a person who is filled with kindness. If you wish to grow in gratitude, do not turn to a grudging person. Surround yourself with godly people who are likeminded and who will share your sufferings in trying times.

b. Which passage struck you most, and why?

Responses will vary depending on personal experience.

2. *Sacred Scripture and the Catholic Church identify seven gifts of the Holy Spirit given to us at baptism and strengthened at confirmation. Read **Isaiah 11** and **CCC 1831.** Reflect on these gifts in the light of godly decision-making. How would the cultivation of these gifts help you when you are facing difficult choices?*

The seven gifts of the Holy Spirit are wisdom, understanding, counsel, fortitude, knowledge, piety, and fear of the Lord. These gifts are given to us at our baptism and are strengthened within us at our confirmation. They sustain us in difficult times and create an interior docility (a supple and teachable spirit) that helps us trust in the Lord. Continuing to cultivate these gifts of the Holy Spirit can help us when we are faced with difficult choices. We can seek out **wisdom** and gain **understanding** through study, prayer, and the **counsel** of godly people. The gift of **fortitude** gives us stability and the strength to face difficulties (and even persecution) with courage and resolve. **Knowledge** of the Faith (a gift further cultivated through studying the *Catechism,* reading Scripture, and actively participating in Mass) reveals truths and gives a providential purpose to whatever challenges enter our lives. **Piety** (loving devotion) and **fear of the Lord** (humble trust in God's providence and power) remind us to put our trust in him during challenging times.

3. *Read **Proverbs 3:5-6, 21-26.** Undue anxiety often keeps us from making decisions. What wisdom do these Scripture passages offer us?*

Once we have sought and received the wisdom of God, we must act. When we step out in faith, trusting the Lord with all our hearts, he will make our paths straight and secure. The Lord can grant us peace of heart and "sweet" sleep, even when the world around us is full of calamity. He is our Confidence and Protector.

4. *Having a well-formed conscience is indispensable in the Christian life. Review what the Church teaches about the conscience in **CCC 1776–1785,** and then use **CCC 1786– 1789** to identify the factors necessary for making good judgments. What struck you most about these passages from the* Catechism?

The conscience, given to us by God, is an inner guide— to love what is good and to avoid evil—that we must accept and obey like the wisdom of a wise counselor. Like any spiritual gift, the conscience must be cultivated and informed through the Word of God and assimilated through faith and prayer. Making moral choices depends on our use of right reason and submission to the Word of God and the teachings of his Church. Sometimes we will face challenging and complex decisions that require prudence, consultation with wise and godly counselors, fervent prayer for the gifts of the Holy Spirit to be awakened within us, and close adherence to the moral teachings of the Faith.

There are some guiding principles that can help us with any decision: (1) One may never commit evil hoping for a good result (the end never justifies an evil means); (2) follow the Golden Rule (do unto others as you would have them do unto you); and (3) finally, let love be the guiding principle, respecting the conscience of others and never acting in a way that causes their consciences to be harmed.

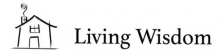 **Living Wisdom**

5. *This week, apply some of the principles discussed in this session to a decision you need to make (it doesn't have to be a big one), and then answer the following questions.*

    a. *Which one of these principles is the most difficult for you to follow?*

    Responses will vary depending on personal experience.

    b. *What did you learn from using this process of decision-making? Be prepared to share your experience with your small group.*

    Responses will vary depending on personal experience.

Session Three

Wisdom in Finances

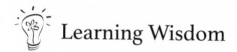 Learning Wisdom

1. *Read* **Proverbs 3:9, 13:11, 28:27, and 29:7 and Sirach 3:30-31, 8:12-13, and 31:5-7.**

   a. What wisdom do you discover on finances?

   The book of Proverbs tells us we are more likely to retain wealth when it is gathered over time than when we receive it in a windfall, and that we should offer the first fruits of our income to the Lord in gratitude. In addition, when we are entrusted with wealth, we should share it generously with the poor.

   From Sirach, we learn that almsgiving not only pleases the Lord and blesses others; it also atones for our sins and prepares us to meet God. Sirach cautions us to take great care in pledging funds ("surety") for another and not to become too focused on or fascinated with wealth because this can lead to sin, ruin, and unhappiness. "He who loves gold will not be justified,

and he who pursues money will be led astray by it"
(Sirach 31:5).

b. *Which passage struck you most, and why?*

Responses will vary depending on personal experience
and insight.

2. *What attitudes toward money (both positive and negative)*
did you inherit from your parents, teachers, or mentors?
How has that wisdom (or folly) influenced your approach
to finances now?

Responses will vary depending on personal experience.

3. *Wealth can be a great blessing, but according to Scripture,*
there are possessions more valuable than money and
much more readily available to us. Read **Sirach 40:19-27.**

a. *What are the blessings on this list?*

Some of the blessings Sirach lists in these verses
include finding and loving wisdom; having a happy
marriage to a devoted and sensible spouse; having
the love of good friends; possessing a pure tongue;
enjoying the fruits of one's labor; being a charitable
person; having sound judgment; and fearing the Lord.

b. *Which blessing resonates with you most, and why?*

Responses will vary based on personal experience.

4. *If it is not viewed in its proper perspective, money can become a kind of idol.* **CCC 2113, 2172, 2424, and 2536** *address the dangers of worshiping money. What can we learn from these passages?*

The most common "idols" today are not carved statues, but things like power, pleasure, and possessions that we allow to capture our hearts. Our hearts are made for God alone. Keeping the Sabbath (Sunday) protects us from the danger of idolizing wealth. Economic systems that put profits ahead of human beings are the source of much conflict, the objectification of people, the worship of wealth, and even atheism. Obedience to the tenth commandment ("Thou shall not covet") helps us act against avarice and injustice.

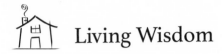 Living Wisdom

5. *Charity and care for the poor are the marks of a wise person who understands the heart of the Lord. Read **Sirach 4:10** and **Proverbs 14:31**. What are a few ways your parish community is caring for those most in need of God's mercy? Participate in one of these ministries this week or make a concrete plan to give your time, talent, or treasure to one or more of them. Be prepared to share your experiences or intentions with your small group.*

Responses will vary depending on the ministries offered by the parish, diocese or wider community. They may include soup kitchens, food banks, shelters, nursing homes, hospices, financial "sponsoring" of a child in need, and partnership with parishes in third world countries.

Session Four

Wisdom
in Relationships

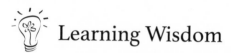 Learning Wisdom

1. *The first and most important relationship to cultivate is our
    relationship with God.* **Proverbs 14:26** *says, "In the fear of
    the L*ORD *one has strong confidence, and his children will
    have a refuge" (also see Proverbs 20:7).*

    a. *Why is fear of the Lord—in our public and private
        lives—possibly the most important gift we can give our
        children and grandchildren?*

    When we have a healthy, happy relationship with the
    Lord, it positively impacts all our human relationships.
    When our children see us practicing our faith in
    private prayer, in family devotions, and in our public
    lives, they are more likely to embrace faith as an
    integrative relationship of love. Our own ignorance of
    or indifference to faith or our inconsistent actions in

public versus private can lead our children to reject the message of the gospel.

b. *Share an experience where the lived faith of a parent, grandparent, or mentor helped your own budding faith to mature.*

Responses will vary depending on personal experience.

2. *The discipline of children is a "hot-button" topic today. However, most people would agree that responsible parenting includes clearly defined and reasonable consequences for disobedient behavior (see Proverbs 29:15).*

a. *Read **Proverbs 13:24, 19:18, 22:6, and 22:15** and record what you learn. According to the wisdom literature, why is disciplining children so important?*

Discipline is a sign of parental love. (It is important to note that "the rod" can be understood to be the guiding rod of a shepherd and not necessarily corporal punishment.) Providing loving discipline to our children when they are young will drive foolishness from their hearts and can be a source of hope for us that they will follow what we have taught them when they are adults.

b. *Share how measured discipline received as a child positively shaped you or someone you know into adulthood?*

Responses will vary depending on personal experience.

3. *Choosing good, wise friends is a common theme in the wisdom literature. The best friends are not only with us through good times and bad, but they help us see our spiritual blind spots. "Faithful are the wounds of a friend" (Proverbs 27:6).*

a. *Read **Sirach 6:5-17 and 9:10.** What do you learn from these passages about the importance of choosing good friends and mentors?*

Kindness and pleasantness in speech attracts friends. One should not enter friendships hastily but rather should allow time for trust to be established. We should avoid fair-weather friends and making enemies. Real friends are a "sturdy shelter" (Sirach 6:14) in life's storms, a priceless treasure, and an "elixir of life" (Sirach 6:16). Fearing the Lord gives us the wisdom to choose good friends and shapes those relationships in a godly direction. Nothing can compare to a lifelong friend: "Forsake not an old friend, for a new one does not compare with him. A new friend is like new wine; when it has aged you will drink it with pleasure" (Sirach 9:10).

b. *Describe the significance of solid friendships in your own faith life.*

Responses will vary depending on personal experience.

 ## Living Wisdom

4. *After reflecting on the topic of healthy, life-giving relationships this week, identify a relationship you want to improve. What is one thing you can do this week to nourish and strengthen that relationship?*

Responses will vary.

5. *Take a few moments this week to reach out to a friend or family member (living or dead) and express your appreciation for his or her role in your life. Consider sharing your experience with your small group.*

Wisdom for Peace of Mind

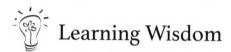

Learning Wisdom

1. *Sirach reminds us that reverence of the Lord produces peace (see Sirach 1:18), and the psalmist confirms, "Great peace have those who love thy law; nothing can make them stumble" (Psalm 119:165). Share an example from a figure in Scripture or from your experience where rejecting God or disobeying him destroyed someone's peace.*

   Responses will vary. Scripture is filled with examples of peace being shattered because of disobedience to God's commands. Some examples include the fall of our first parents, Adam and Eve, and the disobedience of Cain and Abel, the Hebrew people in the desert, Saul, David, and others.

2. *Wisdom literature regularly reminds us that peace can be found, in part, through controlling our anger. Read **Proverbs 19:11 and 29:11** and **Sirach 27:30**.*

a. *What do these verses reveal about the relationship between peace and anger?*

Cultivating the virtue of prudence (good sense) and learning to overlook offenses aid us in avoiding angry behavior. These virtues help us to avoid public "venting" of anger and to use restraint in expressing our emotions. A life driven by anger and wrath is repugnant to the Lord.

b. *The Catechism also connects these two realities (peace and anger). Read **CCC 2302–2306**. What do you discover about the relationship between personal peace and peace in our world?*

Anger over injustice in the world that leads to positive action is praiseworthy, but anger that is transformed into hatred (a desire to inflict evil, violence, or even death upon another) can become a mortal sin. Peace is attained when we unite righteous anger against injustice with concrete acts of charity. These include respect for and development of human life, safeguarding people's goods, upholding human dignity, promoting fraternity among peoples, and cultivating open communication. Any real earthly peace attained is the "fruit of the peace of Christ, the messianic 'Prince of Peace'" (CCC 2305).[1]

3. *One of the other great thieves of our peace is the vice of envy. We can become consumed with what we do not have or envious of others and their possessions.*

a. *Read* **Wisdom 2:24** *and* **Proverbs 23:17, 24:1-2, and 27:20** *and record what you learn.*

Envy was introduced into the world by Satan. Avoid envying or associating with sinners for "their minds devise violence, and their lips talk of mischief" (Proverbs 24:2). Instead, live in fear of the Lord. Never being satisfied with what we have and desiring the goods of others (envy) seems to be part of the human condition. The Catholic Church teaches us that envy can be countered with the cultivation of gratitude and charity—desiring, above all, the good of another.

b. *The Church shares its wisdom on the nature and dangers of envy in* **CCC 2538-2540.** *What do you discover from these paragraphs?*

Envy is a violation of the tenth commandment and must be banished from our hearts. Unchecked envy

---

[1]   Isaiah 9:5.

can lead to the gravest of sins. In the case of King David, it resulted in adultery and murder. The sin of envy is the source of many other vices, including hatred, calumny, and delighting in the misfortune of others. We resist envy by cultivating the love of God, performing concrete acts of goodwill, and exercising humility of heart.

4. *St. Paul, a New Testament sage, was no stranger to difficulty and pain, yet he never lost his peace. Read* **Philippians 4:4-9.** *What wisdom does the apostle offer us for maintaining and sustaining our peace?*

St. Paul maintained his peace by cultivating an attitude of joy, patiently enduring difficult circumstances (forbearance), and resisting anxiety through continual prayer and thanksgiving. These virtues acted like a fortress of peace, guarding his heart and mind in Christ Jesus. The apostle also recognized that focusing on virtuous thoughts (whatever is true, just, pure, excellent) drives out undue anxieties that can rob us of our peace.

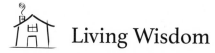 **Living Wisdom**

5. *Jesus said, "Blessed are the peacemakers, for they shall be called sons of God" (Matthew 5:9). What are some concrete ways that we, as members of the Church, can promote peace in our parishes and communities?*

Responses will vary and will be specific to the individual's community and circumstances.

6. *Within the Mass, the priest prays that the sacrifice of Christ will "order our days in [God's] peace" and "advance the peace and salvation of all the world," and we are often challenged at the close of the Liturgy to "go in peace, glorifying the Lord by your life." How have the sacraments of the Church contributed to your peace and aided you in being a peacemaker?*

Responses will vary depending on personal experience.

Session Six

Wisdom in Speech

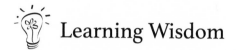 Learning Wisdom

1. *Share an experience when you were hurt by someone's words and a time when you were blessed by someone's words.*

   Responses will vary depending on personal experience.

2. *The book of Sirach offers excellent advice on how to use the tongue wisely. Read **Sirach 4:23-25, 5:10-14, 21:16-17, and 28:12-16** and record the wisdom you find.*

   Sirach advises us that while we should not speak out of turn, it *is* important to speak out at crucial times. Though we should remain silent about topics we are not knowledgeable about, we should share our wisdom with others when we have the opportunity. We should speak truthfully, deliberately, and consistently. A wise person is a good listener. "A fool's narration is like a burden on a journey, but delight will be found in the speech of the intelligent" (Sirach 21:16). The same tongue can be used for good or ill. We should never slander others (i.e., speak false or damaging statements about them). Slander has ruined many lives and livelihoods, toppled cities, and even destroyed nations.

3. *The book of Wisdom reminds us that a "lying mouth destroys the soul" (Wisdom 1:11). What additional insight does the Church offer us into the nature of dishonest speech? (See* **CCC 2482–2487.***)*

Lying has its origin in the devil and is the most direct offense against the truth. Depending on the intention, object, and resulting harm inflicted on another (not to mention the harm against charity and justice), a lie can become a grave sin, breaking our communion with God. Dishonest speech is a kind of verbal violence that can irreparably harm relationships and societies by undermining the trust that forms the fabric of human relationships. Deception denies others the information they need to make good judgments. If we have acted with deception, we have a moral duty as an act of charity and justice to repair the effects of this deception.

4. *The psalmist cries, "I have laid up [hidden] thy word in my heart, that I might not sin against thee" (Psalm 119:11). How*

can committing the Scriptures to memory and treasuring the Word in our hearts help us govern our speech?

Familiarity with the Word of God can begin to shape our own vocabulary and worldview. Memorizing the Scriptures is like establishing a deep wellspring of wisdom and counsel in difficult times. We can draw from it daily, using the Word of God to re-center our hearts in Christ, remind ourselves of the sure promises of God, and recover peace within our hearts.

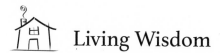 **Living Wisdom**

5. *"Anxiety in a man's heart weighs him down, but a good word makes him glad" (Proverbs 12:25). Take a moment this week to write or call someone in your life whose good work is often overlooked and rarely thanked. Plan your words of encouragement and gratitude so you can communicate your appreciation clearly and confidently. Be prepared to share this or a similar experience with your small group.*

Responses will vary depending on personal experience.

6. *Consider something you have said recently that was received by someone as hurtful or unkind. Take some time this week to reflect on that exchange in prayer, asking the Lord for insight into the situation. Then ask the Lord and the offended party for forgiveness. If you are comfortable, share this or a similar experience with your small group.*

Responses will vary depending on personal experience.

Session Seven

Wisdom in Age

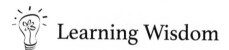 Learning Wisdom

1. *According to divine revelation, what are the responsibilities of those who are mature in faith? Read **Psalm 78:3-7; 1 Timothy 5:9-10; and Titus 2:1-5.***

Older believers are responsible for sharing the faith that was passed on to them (as well as their lived experience of faith) with the coming generations. This personal witness to God's faithfulness can give a strong foundation of faith for their children and grandchildren to grow in hope and obedience. Within the faith community, older Catholics can act as models of child-rearing, hospitality, loving service, and merciful care. They can be examples of temperance, good sense, abiding faith, and love. Young couples with families should be able to look to older believers to teach them reverence, temperance, love of family, chastity, and kindness.

2. *Take a few moments to read through the list of the Ten Commandments in **Exodus 20:2-17.***

a. *Which of the ten commandments is the first to offer us a promise for keeping it?*

The fourth commandment, "Honor your father and your mother."

b. *What is the promise, and why is that significant for us?*

The promise is "that your days may be long in the land which the Lord your God gives you" (Exodus 20:12). The commandment presumes our parents have passed on faith to us. Honoring our parents includes expressing our gratitude to them and obeying their faithful counsel and witness. The language of this promise is similar to what we have seen in the wisdom literature (see Proverbs 3:16). Honoring our parents and living the way of wisdom do not *guarantee* long life (many great saints have died young), but they are the surest, safest path to a happy, peaceful, fulfilled life.

3. *A growing segment of our society is made up of children now caring for their older parents. What wisdom does **Sirach 3:1-16 and 7:27-28** offer them for embracing this opportunity?*

Sirach 3 is a kind of expansion of the promises of the fourth commandment. When we honor our parents, it is reparation for our sins. "Whoever honors his father atones for sins, and whoever glorifies his mother is like one who lays up treasure" (Sirach 3:3-4). The Lord will hear the prayers of those who honor their parents. Honoring our parents also provides us with an opportunity to model joyful service for our own children. We are called to care for our parents happily and without resentment until their natural death. This loving service may be direct or in partnership with professionals or institutions that are best suited for the care that our aging parents need. Sirach 7 invites us to live in gratitude for the gift of life given to us by our parents. Our love and honor can never repay the gifts they have given us.

4. ***Psalm 71*** *was written by a worshiper of advanced age. Spend some time reflecting on this song of praise. What wisdom can you glean from this ancient author?*

The psalmist models an unflinching trust in the Lord as his strength and refuge in times of trouble. His life was marked by continuous praise and proclamation of God's deeds.

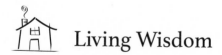 **Living Wisdom**

5. *The book of Sirach advises us not to disregard what older people say because they, too, have learned from their parents (see Sirach 8:9).* ***Sirach 6:34*** *advises us to spend*

time with older people because they are wise. What are some practical ways you can engage mature Catholics in your parish?

Responses will vary depending on personal experience and the parish's dynamic. One answer might be to simply invite older Catholics to be involved in parish activities. They may be waiting to be engaged.

6. *No matter what your age, you can share your wisdom with others:*

    > *God, you have taught me from my youth; to this day I proclaim your wondrous deeds. Now that I am old and gray, do not forsake me, God, that I may program your might to all generations yet to come" (Psalm 71:17-18, NAB).*

Take some time this week to write a summary of the spiritual wisdom you have acquired so far in your life. It does not have to be lengthy. A written record of your spiritual wisdom will be treasured as one of the most important gifts you leave for those you love. Be prepared to share some of what you wrote with your small group.

Responses will vary depending on personal experience.

Session Eight

Wisdom in Christ

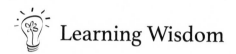 Learning Wisdom

1. Read *Matthew 5:21-26.*

    a. *What advice does Jesus offer regarding the passion of anger?*

    Jesus warns of the dangers of anger, identifying it as a kind of precursor to violence and as something deserving of judgment and punishment. He primarily speaks against anger expressed in verbally abusive language. Anger negatively impacts our relationship with God. We are hypocritical if we approach the altar of God while holding anger or resentment against another. We should reconcile with others quickly before conflict escalates.

    b. *Is there ever a time when anger is justified? Read* **Ephesians 4:26-27** *and* **James 1:19-20.**

Yes, measured and properly motivated anger over injustices in the world can motivate us to courageous action or reform, as we saw in the nonviolent movements of Mahatma Gandhi and Rev. Martin Luther King, Jr. Anger can easily shift to hatred or wrath, so it must be exercised with prudence and guidance.

2. *We learned in an earlier session that the power of life and death are in the tongue. Read **Matthew 5:33-37,** where Jesus specifically addresses honorable speech and oath-taking. According to Jesus, what are the characteristics of honest speech?*

Jesus speaks against rash oath-taking. If we cannot keep our promises, then the oath dishonors the swearer and the object invoked (which is sometimes God himself). The Lord preferred simple speech and actions instead so that a formal oath would be unnecessary.

3. *In Matthew 6, Jesus shares his wisdom on piety and generosity.*

   a. *Read **Matthew 6:1.** What is Jesus' general principle for practicing faith?*

   Jesus tells us that without a motivation to please God alone, public acts of piety will become acts of hollow ritualism (meant to impress onlookers) and will produce no spiritual benefit.

b. Read **Matthew 6:2-18.** *What are the three practices Jesus proposes for his followers?*

Prayer, fasting, and almsgiving form the foundation of Jesus' advice in Matthew 6.

c. *Though we often only associate these three practices with the season of Lent, in what way are they for all seasons, and what vices do they address?*

Although these practices are intensified during the season of Lent, it is clear Jesus intended them to be integral parts of his followers' lives. They help free us from our passions, pride, and possessions. These are the three spiritual pitfalls we see present in the original sin of Adam and Eve and that Jesus resisted when he was tempted by the devil. Prayer, fasting, and almsgiving are like a "triple antibiotic" against the capital vices of pride, greed, gluttony, lust, sloth, envy, and anger.

4. *What wisdom can you glean for prayer and the Christian life from the Our Father prayer in* **Matthew 6:9-15?**

Responses will vary depending on personal experience. They might include: trusting in God as our Father, honoring the Lord's name, praying in a spirit of dependence upon the Lord for our daily needs, maintaining a repentant attitude, quickly forgiving others, and so on.

5. *In St. Paul's first letter to the Corinthians, he compares the wisdom of God in Christ with the wisdom of the world. Read* **1 Corinthians 1:18-30.**

   a. *How are these perspectives different?*

   The world saw the cross of Christ as foolishness and a failure. It did not fit into their preconceived categories of how God would act (in powerful signs or erudite philosophy). To those who understand the wisdom of God, the Cross is power personified and wisdom beyond words. It is a solution beyond human imagination or speculation to effect the salvation of all those who would receive it.

   b. *Who will be the recipient of God's wisdom in Christ, and why is that significant?*

   It is not the most educated, powerful, or well-positioned people who will receive this wisdom but rather those the world perceives as weak and foolish.

By entrusting the wisdom of God in Christ to the lowest and humblest of souls, the Lord ensures there will be no place for personal boasting. Those who receive this gift will proclaim Christ as their wisdom, righteousness, sanctification, and redemption.

 **Living Wisdom**

6. *Jesus proclaimed that the person who listens to and obeys his Word is like a wise man who builds his house on a rock. Read* **Matthew 7:24-27.**

   a. *What parts of the Sermon on the Mount did you find most challenging, and why?*

      Responses will vary depending on personal experience.

   b. *Identify one concrete change you can make in your daily walk with the Lord based on the wisdom of the Sermon on the Mount. Be prepared to share it with your small group.*

My Gathered Wisdom